A SPECIAL GIFT FOR

from

A LOVING GIFT FOR YOUR CHILDREN

a mother's

Legacy

Your Life Story in Your Own Words

Copyright© 2000 by J. Countryman, Inc.,
Puplished under license from J. Countryman®,
a trademark of Thomas Nelson, Inc.

This edition published in 2003 by J. Countryman
exclusively for Hallmark Cards, Inc.
Visit us online at www.Hallmark.com

Project editor: Terri Gibbs

Designed by Koechel Peterson & Associates, Inc., Minneapolis, MN

ISBN: 1404101276 (Hallmark edition)

Printed and bound in China

www.jcountryman.com

Contents

AYS PASS...SEASONS CHANGE...months meld into years, and we stand looking back at our lives—childhood memories, exciting moments, crises, and turning points.

In January we think of new beginnings; in February of valentines, first dates, and first kisses. Does ever a June pass without thoughts of our own wedding day? Surely summer evokes backseat memories of seemingly unending trips to Grandma's house or the beach. And don't November and December bring to mind family traditions and celebrations held tightly through the years?

Like ivy on the garden trellis, our lives are inescapably entwined with the seasons and months of the year. That is why we have designed this mother's memory journal in a twelve-month format. Each month features twelve intriguing questions with space to write a personal answer. Questions explore family history, childhood memories, light-hearted incidents, cherished traditions, and the dreams and spiritual adventures encountered in a lifetime of living.

Whether you choose to complete the journal in a few days, weeks, or over the course of a year, the questions will take you on a journey through the times and seasons of your life. This makes a tangible family record to pass on as a gift to a son or daughter, a loving memoir of written words that are windows to a mother's heart.

No matter what your age, memory and reminiscence open a richer, fuller understanding of who you are as a family. Let this memory journal be a starting point—a door into discussing and sharing the unique qualities of your life. May *A Mother's Legacy* draw you closer to each other as you share the experiences of a lifetime.

YOUR FULL GIVEN NAME

YOUR DATE OF BIRTH

YOUR PLACE OF BIRTH

YOUR MOTHER'S FULL NAME

the place and date of her birth

YOUR FATHER'S FULL NAME

the place and date of his birth

THE NAMES OF YOUR PATERNAL GRANDPARENTS

the places and dates of their births

THE NAMES OF YOUR MATERNAL GRANDPARENTS

the places and dates of their births

THE NAMES OF YOUR SIBLINGS

the places and dates of their births

THE DATE AND PLACE OF YOUR MARRIAGE

THE FULL GIVEN NAME OF YOUR HUSBAND

THE NAMES AND BIRTH DATES OF YOUR CHILDREN

What is your Favorite?

FLOWER

PERFUME

COLOR

HYMN OR SONG

BOOK

AUTHOR

SCRIPTURE, SAYING

OR QUOTATION

DESSERT

VACATION SPOT

TYPE OF FOOD

SPORT

LEISURE ACTIVITY

PERSONAL
PORTRAIT

January

The beauty of the written word

is that it can be held

close to the heart

and read over and over again.

FLORENCE LITTAUER

WHAT WAS YOUR FAVORITE

PASTIME AS A CHILD?

Did you prefer doing it alone

or with someone else?

WHO GAVE YOU

YOUR NAME AND WHY?

DID YOU HAVE

A FAMILY NICKNAME?

HOW DID YOU GET IT?

*Describe
your
childhood
bedroom.
What was
the view
from your
window?*

What was the silliest thing you ever did?

HOW OLD WERE YOU?

What were Sundays like as a child?
Did you go to church?

_____

_____

_____

_____

Visit grandparents?

_____

_____

_____

Was there a family dinner?

_____

_____

_____

If so, what was the typical menu?

_____

_____

_____

_____

_____

_____

WHERE DID YOUR FATHER GO TO WORK EVERY DAY,
and what did he do?

HOW DID YOUR MOTHER SPEND HER DAY?

DID SHE HAVE A JOB OR DO VOLUNTEER

WORK OUTSIDE THE HOME?

DESCRIBE WHAT

THE FAMILY LIVING

ROOM LOOKED

LIKE WHEN

YOU WERE A CHILD.

Did you have a favorite bedtime story or a prayer that you said before you went to sleep? Who tucked you in?

Where was your childhood home?

Did you enjoy living there?

DESCRIBE YOUR GRANDPARENTS' HOUSES.

Did you visit them often?
Why or why not?

LIST ONE SPECIAL

MEMORY

ABOUT EACH

OF YOUR BROTHERS

AND SISTERS.

*Recall for
me some of
the most
important
lessons you
have learned
in life.*

February

For all of us,

today's experiences

are tomorrow's memories.

BARBARA JOHNSON

SHARE A MEMORY OF

YOUR GRANDPARENTS

or an older person you loved.

Who have you turned to for advice
or guidance in your life?

AS A YOUNG GIRL, DID YOU PARTICIPATE
IN CHURCH, SCOUTING, OR
SOME OTHER ORGANIZATION
OR ACTIVITY? *How important a role
did that play in your life?*

Do you remember a special book from your childhood?
A Bible? A storybook?
Who gave it to you? Do you still have it?

DESCRIBE A MEMORABLE
   VALENTINE YOU RECEIVED.

How far did you have to travel to attend
elementary, junior high,
and high school,
and how did you get there?

What scent or sound immediately
takes you back to childhood?

Describe the feeling it evokes.

WHAT WAS YOUR

FAVORITE MEAL WHEN

YOU WERE A CHILD?

WHAT MADE IT

YOUR FAVORITE?

*What was
the name
of your
favorite
pet?
Why was
it your
favorite?*

What chores did you have to do when you were
growing up? Which ones did you dislike
most? Which did you not mind doing?

Did you get an allowance?
How much was it?

TELL ME ABOUT YOUR FIRST JOB.

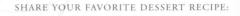

SHARE YOUR FAVORITE DESSERT RECIPE:

SHARE A "BAD WEATHER" STORY—
getting caught in a hailstorm,
living without power,
being housebound for days
during a big snowfall.

March

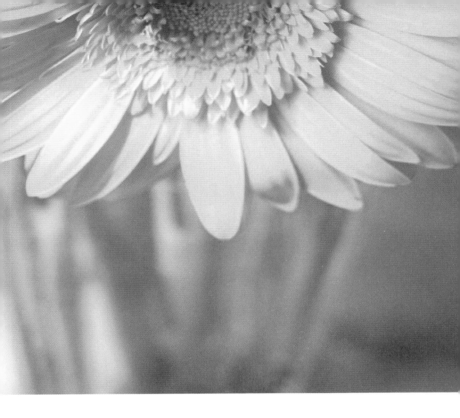

The mother's heart

is the child's schoolroom.

HENRY WARD BEECHER

CAN YOU RECALL AN ESPECIALLY

INTERESTING VISITOR TO YOUR HOME?

*What made that person
or the occasion memorable?*

WHAT DID YOU WANT
TO BE WHEN YOU GREW
UP? HOW OLD WERE
YOU? DID THAT CHANGE
OVER THE YEARS?

*What kinds
of things
do you do
to relax
or renew?
Do you have
a special
place you
like to go?*

WHO WAS YOUR FAVORITE TEACHER?
Why?

DESCRIBE ONE OF YOUR FAVORITE DRESS-UP OUTFITS

AS A CHILD.

ON WHAT OCCASIONS WOULD YOU WEAR IT?

Did you ever have a special hideaway or playhouse?

What made it special?

WHAT EXTRACURRICULAR ACTIVITIES WERE YOU INVOLVED IN DURING HIGH SCHOOL?

Why did you choose those activities?

WHAT WAS

THE HARDEST THING

YOU EVER

HAD TO DO?

What crazy fads do you remember in grade school?

When did you have your first date? Tell me about it.

WHAT DO YOU REMEMBER ABOUT YOUR FIRST KISS?

What did you do to celebrate birthdays
   when you were growing up?

Record here some gardening or decorating tips
that you have found helpful:

April

However time or circumstance

may come between a mother

and her child,

their lives are interwoven forever.

PAM BROWN

WHAT WERE SOME OF THE MOST

MEMORABLE BOOKS

YOU READ AS A CHILD?

What made them memorable?

What were your family finances like
when you were growing up?

How did that affect you?

TELL ABOUT AN AWARD OR HONOR
OR SPECIAL RECOGNITION
YOU HAVE RECEIVED.

WHAT MISCHIEVOUS

CHILDHOOD EXPERIENCE

DO YOU REMEMBER?

HOW DID IT

AFFECT YOU?

What meaningful advice did you receive from an adult? What were the circumstances?

As a teenager did you rebel
or do things your parents
wouldn't have approved of?

How do you feel about that now?

When did you first learn about sex?

What was your reaction?

WHAT THINGS DO YOU WISH
        YOU HAD DONE IN CHILDHOOD
        OR ADOLESCENCE?

WHAT ARE THE THINGS
YOU ARE MOST GLAD YOU TRIED?

DESCRIBE YOUR

MOTHER

IN HER

BEST DRESS.

*Describe
your father
in his
working
clothes.*

What did your family like to do on weekends?

Describe one particularly memorable event.

SHARE ONE OF YOUR MOTHER'S BEST RECIPES

or a recipe for one of your
favorite childhood dishes.

May

In search of my mother's garden,

I found my own.

ALICE WALKER

WHAT TOYS DID YOU LIKE TO PLAY WITH?

Why those particular toys?

What is one of the most difficult choices
you ever had to make?

Would you make the same choice again?

DO YOU REMEMBER A TIME WHEN YOU FELT PARTICULARLY UNSURE OR CONFUSED?

What did you do?

DID YOU

EVER GO TO

A DANCE?

TELL ME ABOUT IT.

*What
kind of car
did your
family drive?
Were you
proud of
it or
embarrassed
by it?
Why?*

Did you attend family reunions?

Share a memory of one.

Did you go to church or community potlucks?

_____
_____
_____
_____

*How were they important to you
and your family?* _____

_____
_____
_____
_____
_____
_____
_____
_____
_____
_____
_____
_____
_____
_____
_____
_____

Tell about someone
   who influenced your life profoundly.

TELL ME ABOUT YOUR BEST CHILDHOOD FRIEND.

Tell me about your best childhood friend. Where did you meet?

What secrets did you share?

What did you like to do?

IF YOU WENT TO

COLLEGE OR TO A

CAREER TRAINING

SCHOOL, WHERE DID

YOU GO AND WHY?

_Where did
you live
when you
were going
to college or
developing
a career?
Describe an
unforgettable
experience
from that
time in
your life._

MAY

WHAT WERE YOUR YOUTHFUL GOALS
AND AMBITIONS FOR LIFE?
Which ones have you been able to fulfill?

ARE THERE CERTAIN SCRIPTURES OR OTHER WRITINGS

THAT YOU REPEATEDLY TURN TO FOR

INSPIRATION OR GUIDANCE?

June

Rings and jewels are not gifts,

but apologies for gifts.

The only gift

is a portion of thyself.

RALPH WALDO EMERSON

IF YOU LEARNED TO PLAY

A MUSICAL INSTRUMENT,

TELL ME YOUR MEMORIES

OF LESSONS, PRACTICE,

AND YOUR MUSIC TEACHER.

If not, what instrument

did you want to play and why?

WHAT FASHIONS WERE

POPULAR WHEN YOU

WERE IN HIGH SCHOOL?

DID YOU LIKE THEM?

WHY OR WHY NOT?

*How old
were you
when you
met Dad,
and what
attracted
you
to him?*

When did you first know you wanted to marry him?

What made you feel that way?

SHARE A MEMORY ABOUT THE WAY
HE PROPOSED TO YOU.

June

WHAT DID

YOU WEAR

ON YOUR

WEDDING DAY?

*Tell me
about your
wedding
day, from
beginning
to end.*

DID YOUR WEDDING CEREMONY

include a special vow to each other?

_____

_____

_____

_____

_____

_____

_____

What was the significance of it?

_____

_____

_____

_____

_____

_____

_____

Where did you go on your honeymoon?

Share one humorous incident.

What was your first house or apartment together like?

DO YOU REMEMBER ONE
        OF THE MEALS YOU FIXED
AFTER YOU WERE MARRIED?
How has your cooking changed since then?

WHAT DO YOU LOVE BEST ABOUT DAD NOW?

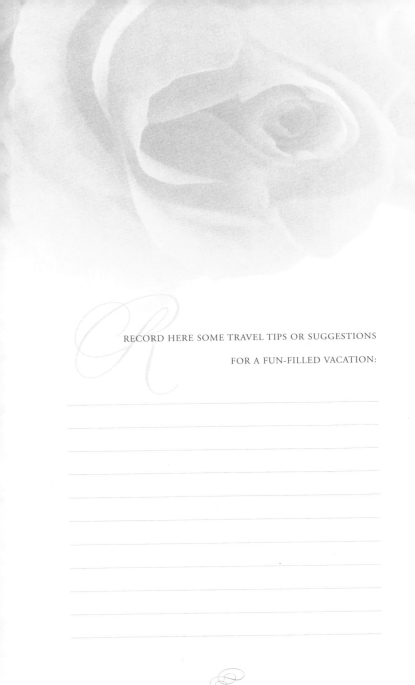

RECORD HERE SOME TRAVEL TIPS OR SUGGESTIONS

FOR A FUN-FILLED VACATION:

July

look back and see

how I've become who I am

by a family that found

sweetness and joy somewhere inside when...

life experience tasted bitter.

KATHY BOICE

SHARE A FAMILY TRADITION

OR MEMORY

FROM THE FOURTH OF JULY.

Have you ever participated in a rally
or demonstration? _____

_____

_____

_____

What was the cause? _____

_____

_____

_____

_____

Why did you participate? _____

_____

_____

_____

_____

_____

_____

_____

_____

WHO IN YOUR FAMILY SERVED
IN THE MILITARY AND WHEN?

Do you have a special memory of that person?

DID YOU LEARN

TO SWIM?

HOW?

Did you take family vacations? Record one especially memorable experience.

Tell about your first trip by plane, train, or ship.

_____

_____

_____

_____

_____

_____

_____

How old were you? _____

_____

_____

Were you excited? Nervous? _____

_____

_____

_____

_____

_____

_____

_____

_____

_____

IF YOU EVER TRAVELED ABROAD, WHAT WAS THE MOST UNIQUE EXPERIENCE OF THE TRIP?

If you haven't been abroad, what foreign country would you most like to visit? Why? Did you visit them often? Why or why not?

DESCRIBE THE MOST FASCINATING PLACE YOU HAVE VISITED.

TELL ABOUT A DRIVING TRIP WITH YOUR FAMILY.

*Did your relatives come to visit
in the summer or did you go to visit them?*

What are your memories of those visits?

HOW DID YOU LEARN TO DRIVE?

What was your first car like?

DID A TRAGEDY

EVER STRIKE

YOUR FAMILY?

HOW WERE

YOU AFFECTED?

Share a
favorite
poem or
a passage
of writing
that
has been
especially
meaningful
in your life:

August

The family—

that dear octopus from whose tentacles

we never quite escape,

nor, in our inmost hearts, ever quite wish to.

DODIE SMITH

NAME A BOOK OR AUTHOR

THAT HELPED YOU DEVELOP

A PHILOSOPHY OF LIFE.

Share some of those insights.

Did you have a collection when you were growing up?

_____

_____

_____

_____

_____

_____

_____

_____

_____

_____

What initially sparked
your interest in it? _____

_____

_____

_____

_____

_____

_____

_____

_____

DESCRIBE A PERFECT SUMMER DAY.

August

WHAT KIND OF

OUTDOOR WORK

DO YOU LIKE?

HATE? WHY?

If you could be a patron of a charity or organization, which one would you choose? Why?

When did you learn how to ride a bike,

OR TO WATER SKI, SNOW SKI, ROLLER SKATE, OR SAIL?

Share your memories of the experience.

What summer games and activities
did your family enjoy?

Did you ever milk a cow
    or spend time on a farm or in the country?

_____

_____

_____

*Tell me about it.*_____

_____

_____

_____

_____

_____

_____

_____

_____

_____

_____

_____

_____

_____

_____

DESCRIBE YOUR FIRST TRIP ALONE.

WHAT PLACES

WOULD YOU STILL

LIKE TO VISIT?

WHY?

Describe a frightening or difficult experience from childhood. How did you respond to it?

TELL ME ABOUT YOUR MOST
UNFORGETTABLE SUMMER
EXPERIENCE AS A CHILD.

SHARE SOME OF YOUR IDEAS

ABOUT SUCCESSFUL ENTERTAINING:

September

Our lives are a mosaic of little things,

like putting a rose

in a vase on the table.

INGRID TROBISCH

DID YOU LEARN TO SEW

OR MAKE OTHER CRAFTS?

How and when?

What was the first thing you made?

TELL ABOUT

A SPECIAL OUTING

YOU TOOK WITH

YOUR MOTHER

OR YOUR FATHER.

*What was
the most
tender day
in your
childhood?*

What were your favorite subjects in grade school

junior high

high school?

What was your major in college?

Would you choose that major again? Why or why not?

AS A YOUNG PERSON DID YOU VOLUNTEER

for work in church, community,
or social services?

Tell me about your experiences.

When did you move away from home? _____

_____

_____

_____

Describe where you lived
    and how you felt about it. _____

_____

_____

_____

_____

_____

_____

_____

_____

_____

_____

_____

_____

_____

_____

_____

WHO WAS YOUR BEST FRIEND AFTER YOU WERE MARRIED?

*Describe some of the fun things
you did together. Are you still friends?*

WHAT IS SOMETHING

YOU LEARNED

FROM AN ESPECIALLY

DIFFICULT TIME

IN YOUR LIFE?

*What is
something
you learned
from an
especially
happy
time
in your
life?*

WHAT SPECIAL TALENTS DID YOUR PARENTS NURTURE IN YOU?

How have you developed those talents?

What would you like to learn to do?

Why?

WHAT WOULD

YOU DO

DIFFERENTLY

IN LIFE

IF YOU COULD?

Describe
your personal
style in
clothing,
makeup,
skin care,
hair care.

October

How will our children know who they are

if they don't know

where they came from?

MA IN GRAPES OF WRATH

WHO ARE SOME OF

THE BEST SPEAKERS

YOU HAVE EVER HEARD?

Why?

October

HOW WOULD YOU
LIKE TO BE
REMEMBERED?
WHY IS THIS
IMPORTANT TO YOU?

What are some of the things that make you smile when you think of them?

WHAT DO YOU CONSIDER
to be some of life's most difficult challenges?

WHAT DO YOU CONSIDER TO BE LIFE'S GREATEST GIFTS?

What responsibilities did your parents
require of you as a child?

EXPLAIN HOW THIS AFFECTED YOUR GROWTH AND DEVELOPMENT.

NAME YOUR FAVORITE HOBBY.
WHEN AND WHERE
DID YOU START DOING IT?

Why do you enjoy it?

When and where did you buy your first house?

*Describe the house and explain
     any significance it held for you.*

WHAT IS THE STRANGEST THING
YOU HAVE EVER SEEN?

Tell about a memorable hotel
or resort you have visited. Describe the location
AND TELL ABOUT EXPERIENCES THAT WERE SIGNIFICANT.

DID YOU EVER GO ON A HAYRIDE OR BOB FOR APPLES?

What other fun activities did you
and your friends or classmates enjoy?

As a teenager, did you belong
to a club or church youth group?

Tell me about the individuals
in the group who were
most significant to you.

SHARE SOME HELPFUL HOME REMEDIES

or tips for good health:

November

In our family an experience was not finished,

nor truly experienced,

unless written down

or shared with another.

ANNE MORROW LINDBERGH

WHAT INDIVIDUALS HAVE HAD

THE GREATEST IMPACT

ON YOUR LIFE?

In what way?

WHAT IS YOUR

MOST TREASURED

POSSESSION

AND WHY?

Who were your female role models when you were growing up? How have they affected the kind of person you are?

WHAT IS YOUR MOST VIVID MEMORY
OF BEING PREGNANT?

HOW DID YOU CHOOSE MY NAME AND WHY?

WHAT IS YOUR MOST POIGNANT MEMORY ABOUT MY CHILDHOOD?

What was a favorite
Thanksgiving tradition
in your family?

WHAT ARE SOME
THINGS FROM
YOUR CHILDHOOD
THAT YOU ARE
THANKFUL FOR?

What childhood memory first comes to mind when you think about winter? How do you respond to that memory?

What are some of the things you remember most
from your childhood

EXPERIENCES AT CHURCH OR SCHOOL

OR IN YOUR NEIGHBORHOOD?

Do certain people come to mind?

What family custom would you like to pass on
to your children and grandchildren?

WHAT NEW TRADITION
WOULD YOU LIKE TO
START IN THE FAMILY?
WHAT IS ITS
SIGNIFICANCE?

Share a favorite Thanksgiving or Christmas recipe.

December

If everything special and warm and happy

in my formative years

could have been consolidated

into one word,

that word would have been Christmas.

GLORIA GAITHER

TELL ABOUT

SOME CHRISTMAS RITUALS

IN YOUR FAMILY

and how you felt about them.

WERE YOU EVER IN A

CHRISTMAS PROGRAM?

HOW DID YOU

RESPOND TO

THE EXPERIENCE?

_What
favorite
Christmas
treasures
have you
kept from
year to year?
Share their
origins._

Tell about a memorable
   Christmas visit with relatives.

WHAT IS YOUR FAVORITE CHRISTMAS CAROL?

Why?

Did you have a Christmas stocking
as a child or a special ornament?

What did it look like?

DESCRIBE THE CHRISTMAS

that has been the most meaningful to you.

WHAT WOULD BE

THE MOST

WONDERFUL GIFT

YOU COULD RECEIVE?

WHY?

*What have
people older
than you
taught you
about life?
What have
you learned
from children
and young
people?*

WHAT WOULD YOU LIKE TO SEE HAPPEN
in the next ten years?

WHAT WAS ONE OF THE BEST SURPRISES YOU EVER HAD?

A PARTY? A GIFT? AN UNEXPECTED FAVOR?

DID YOU EVER SURPRISE SOMEONE ELSE?

IN WHAT WAY?

What word best describes your life?

EXPLAIN WHY.

What advice about life would you give to others?

PHOTOS

PHOTOS

PHOTOS